CAMPBELL MORRIS

Fold Your Own Boats

Illustrations:
MARK DAVID

Model diagrams:
CAMPBELL MORRIS

HARPER COLLINS

To Claudine and Natalie,
me little hearties

Harper Collins
London - Glasgow - New York
Sydney - Auckland - Toronto
Johannesburg

First published in Australia in 1990 by
Angus & Robertson Publishers
A division of HarperCollinsPublishers (Australia) Pty Limited

This edition published by
Harper Collins 1991

Copyright © Campbell Morris 1990

ISBN 0.00.196385.6

Typeset in 10pt Aristocrat Light by Midland Typesetters, Victoria
Printed by Griffin Press, Adelaide, South Australia

 5   4   3   2   1
95 94 93 92 91

CAMPBELL MORRIS

Fold Your Own Boats

Important notice to all boating enthusiasts
Some of the boats in this book are rather complicated to make. It is really important to practise all the basic steps until you feel confident about them before starting on the boats themselves.

Introduction

Ahoy there, me little sea captains!

For thousands of years people have crossed the waters of the globe in boats and ships of all shapes and sizes—kayaks and canoes, galleys and galleons, sailing ships and steam ships, fishing boats and battleships, junks, yachts and rowing boats, and luxurious passenger liners.

Stories of romance and adventure on the high seas abound. There are tales of the Vikings who traded and plundered; of the Spaniards who sailed their galleons in search of treasure and lands to conquer; of intrepid explorers who circum-navigated the globe in sailing ships; and of villainous pirates who struck fear into the heart of many a sailor.

If you are an aspiring seafarer, if you love the feel of wind in your hair and salt spray on your face, or if you just love mucking about in boats, then welcome to the magic world of paper watercraft. With the models shown in this book, you will be able to create your own nautical adventures in boating ponds, or even the bath. Rubber ducks beware!

I have many models to show you, each simply described and illustrated so that, with practice, even the clumsiest deckhands will be creating their own paper watercraft. Once you have folded the models successfully and 'know the ropes', I encourage you to invent new models.

Believe it or not, this book outlines some of the basic geometry used in shipbuilding. Once you have mastered the paper models you may like to try your hand at cardboard or wooden boats. The shapes are the same, only the material differs! You can even go on to make life-size versions. Get your friends and some adults involved; after you've enjoyed building, you'll enjoy learning to sail. (Please make sure your craft is waterproof first!)

Finally, read the instructions carefully and practise the folds shown at the front of the book before you start. Once you have mastered the basic steps, you won't be left high and dry!

Happy folding and bon voyage!

Types of Paper to Use

The models in this book all employ standard A4 (210 mm x 197 mm) paper, which is used in its rectangular form or cut to make a square. Of course, you can use any size you like and any paper you like as long as it is crisp and relatively heavy. You don't have to be restricted to plain white paper. For example, you can use wax paper, which will give your vessel greater water resistance. Cellophane paper can also look great when folded.

A waterproof lacquer spray is available in most hardware stores so that you can protect your models and make them last longer in water.

Battleships are more suited to the metallic look of aluminium foil. However, as aluminium foil is difficult to fold, I suggest you glue a sheet of ordinary paper to one side, using spray adhesive. When the adhesive is dry your foil will have the rigidity to allow you to fold a really strong battleship. Some chocolates are wrapped in foil which is already backed with paper and this is ideal for folding. (And you can eat the chocolate too!)

Folding Techniques

Try all the basic steps several times before starting. Then, when you feel confident, begin on the boats themselves.

SYMBOLS AND PROCEDURES

Basic symbols and procedures have been included at the bottom of each project.

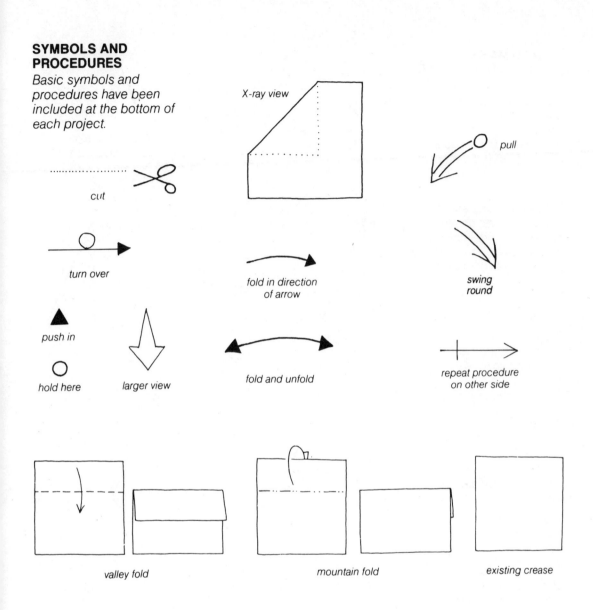

cut

X-ray view

pull

turn over

fold in direction of arrow

swing round

push in

hold here

larger view

fold and unfold

repeat procedure on other side

valley fold

mountain fold

existing crease

HOW TO MAKE A SQUARE

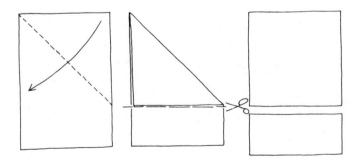

HOW TO MAKE
AN INSIDE REVERSE FOLD

Some of the smaller folds require patience. By practising with small pieces of paper you can gain experience in making the perfect boat—to the finest detail.

1.
Fold a paper square in half diagonally then unfold. It should look like this with a crease down the centre. Fold the two sides in towards the centre.

2.
Fold the model in half.

3.
Fold the top corner towards you along the line.

4.
Crease and unfold.

5.
Fold the top corner away from you along the same line.

6.
Crease and unfold.

7.
The model is now creased ready for the inside reverse fold.

8.
Open the model at the top, push the peak down.

9.
The centre of the peak folds inwards.

10.
Almost there.

11.
A completed inside reverse fold.

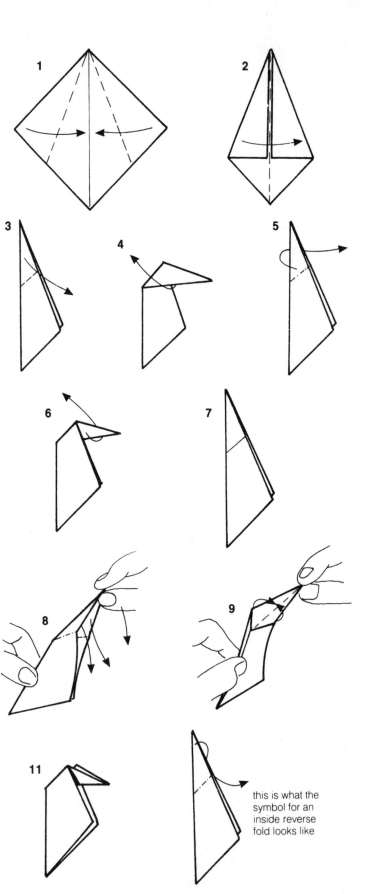

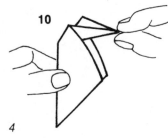

this is what the symbol for an inside reverse fold looks like

1

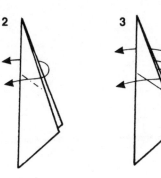

2

3

HOW TO MAKE AN OUTSIDE REVERSE FOLD

Another common folding procedure. Start with steps 1 and 2 of the inside reverse fold.

1.
Fold towards you and unfold.

2.
Fold away from you and unfold.

3.
Open out the model.

4.
Push in at this point.

5.
Pull the top corner outwards.

6.
The model from the other side—while pulling back the top, bring the bottom two corners together.

7a. and 7b.
Two views of the completed model.

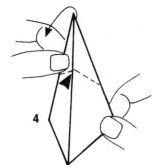

4

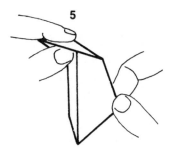

5

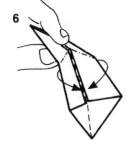

6

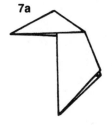

7a

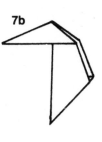

7b

this is what the symbol for an outside reverse fold looks like

HOW TO MAKE
A RABBIT EAR FOLD

1.
Using a small square of paper, fold in the sides to the centre.

2.
Valley fold and unfold.

3.
Valley fold the opposite side and unfold.

4.
Valley fold the corner to the centre of the creases to make a point—the 'rabbit ear'.

5.
Fold or push the model in along crease lines.

6.
Almost there.

7.
It's complete!

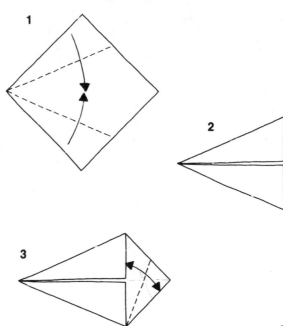

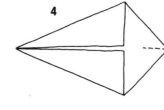

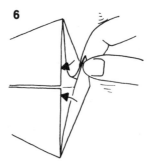

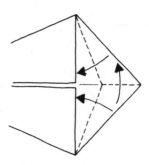

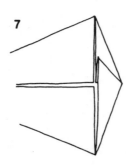

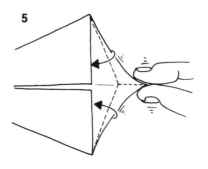

this is what the symbol for a rabbit ear fold looks like

HOW TO PUSH IN YOUR BOAT

The "push in" technique is used in many boats in this book. It's a little tricky so follow the steps carefully.

1.
To carry out the push in procedure, we must first make a "sample" boat. Take a square of paper and fold it in half diagonally both ways and once in half behind as shown.

2.
Bring the sides in and flatten the top.

3.
This is known as the waterbomb base. Turn the model over.

4.
Carry out the push in procedure as shown. Crease fold over and behind where shown.

5.
Hold the sides and open out the model. Push in the centre and new sides as shown.

6.
Flatten the model and turn over.

7.
A completed "boat" that will float!

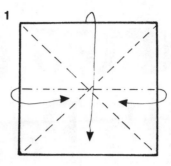

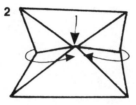

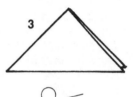

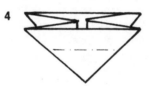

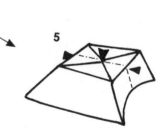

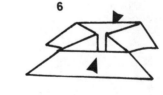

Games to Play with Paper Boats

Battle in the Bath

This game is ideal for younger children and can involve the whole family. It's great fun in the bath, but your bathroom may resemble an ocean if you're not careful. One person sits at one end of the bath while another person sits at the other end. These two blow onto a sailing boat and try to make it sail back and forth between each other. Their task is made difficult, however, by a third person who sits in the middle and blows another sailing boat to try to intercept the first boat and cause a collision. Try it with the catamaran on page 26 of this book—you'll have your very own America's Cup battle.

Round and Round the Sink We Go!

This is an interesting game to play when the weather is not good enough to go outside. You can experiment with wave motion and direction by filling a sink or bath with water. Pull out the plug and watch the boats go round and round until they are finally sucked into the plughole. If you do this a few times, you will notice that the whirlpool always goes in the same direction. Did you know that the whirlpool goes in the opposite direction in the Southern Hemisphere? This is due to the rotation of the Earth!

8

Midwater Landings

The idea behind this game is to land the sea-plane shown in this book (or any other paper aircraft) onto an aircraft carrier floating in the middle of a boating pond or garden pool. Make a large version of the aircraft carrier (page 44) out of waterproof paper and launch it into the middle of your "sea". This game is ideal for school or parties as many people can play. Each contestant has five flying models and takes it in turns to throw one model at a time. Make sure you mark the planes clearly so that you know which is which. The person who lands the most aircraft on the carrier is the winner.

The Great String Race

For this game you need to divide a pool or pond into lanes, one lane for each player. Use string held in place by rocks or bricks to form the lanes in your pool. Each contestant chooses their best model and attaches a string or fishing line to the boat. The boats are left at one end of the pool and the contestants, holding the string or fishing line, go to the other end. The first person to reel in their boat is the winner. This race is a good test of water resistance. If your boat is slower than the others, it may be because it has a wider hull which will meet greater water resistance. If you reel in your boat too fast, it may meet water resistance and sink!

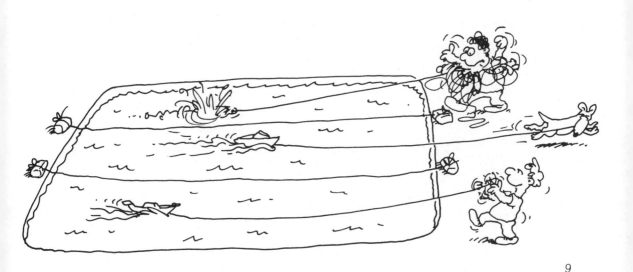

Canoe

Now you can have your very own dugout canoe. Imagine braving the rapids as your canoe carries a load of leaves or even snails. If you make a large version of this canoe, it will look like a tanker. Why not make a couple of paper boxes to place upside down in your tanker to look like cargo?

1.
Begin with an A4 size piece of paper. Fold horizontally in half.

2.
Turn over the folded corners as shown, about 2.5 cm.

3.
Fold the top flap down so that it partly covers the folded corners.

4.
With the model turned over, fold sides in as shown.

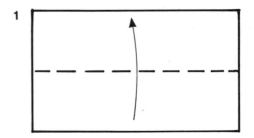

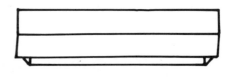

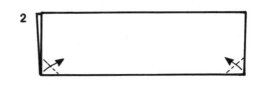

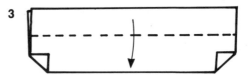

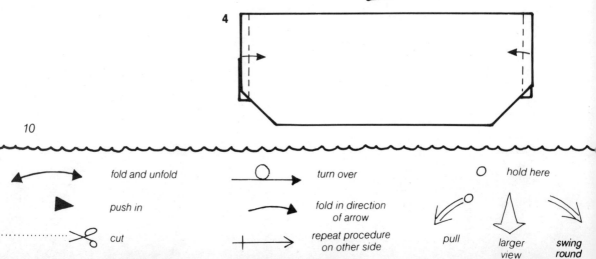

fold and unfold	turn over	○ hold here
push in	fold in direction of arrow	pull
cut	repeat procedure on other side	larger view swing round

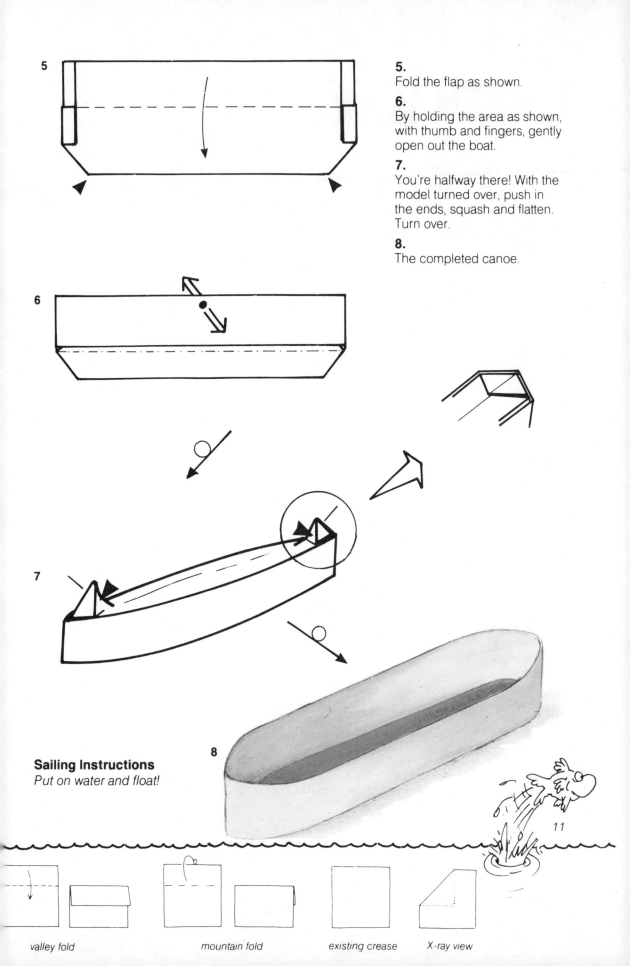

5.
Fold the flap as shown.

6.
By holding the area as shown, with thumb and fingers, gently open out the boat.

7.
You're halfway there! With the model turned over, push in the ends, squash and flatten. Turn over.

8.
The completed canoe.

Sailing Instructions
Put on water and float!

11

valley fold   mountain fold   existing crease   X-ray view

Gondola

If you lived in Venice, chances are you might catch a gondola to school, not a car or a bus. You'd have no trouble keeping afloat with this great model.

1.
Using a square piece of paper, fold the corner as shown.

2. and 2a.
Fold the point as shown and repeat for the other corner.

3.
Larger view. Fold the corners behind.

4.
Fold the model horizontally in half.

5.
Inverse fold both ends along the inside folds.

6.
Tape or staple the ends together and make rabbit ear folds as shown.

7.
Open your gondola out and round out shelter A. Tape the points together—X marks the spot.

8.
Your finished gondola

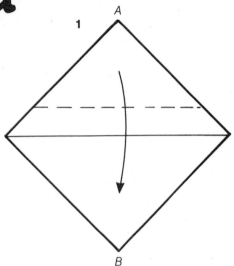

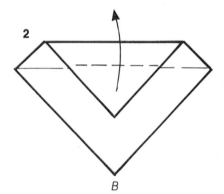

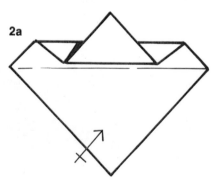

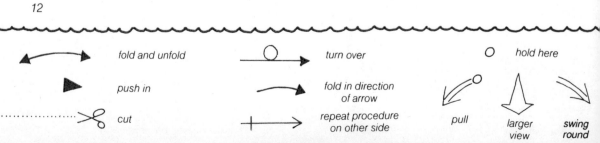

fold and unfold	turn over
push in	fold in direction of arrow
cut	repeat procedure on other side

hold here

pull

larger view

swing round

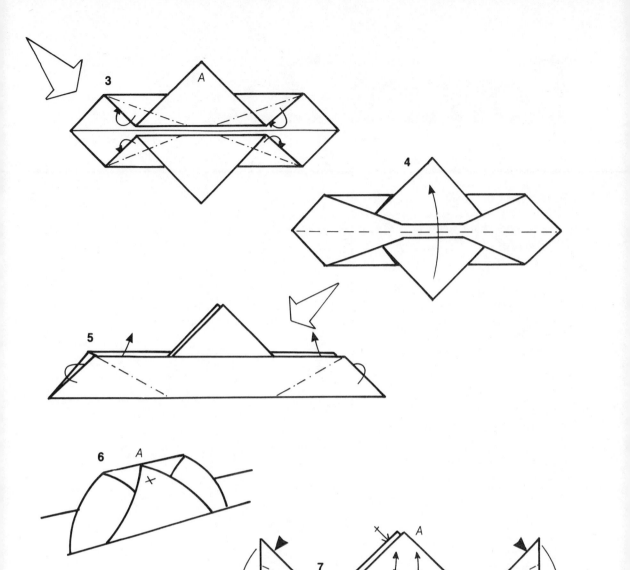

3

A

4

5

6 A
×

7 A
×
×

Sailing Instructions

*Your gondola may need
some weight for ballast. Why
not send a couple of snails
on a romantic ride.*

8

13

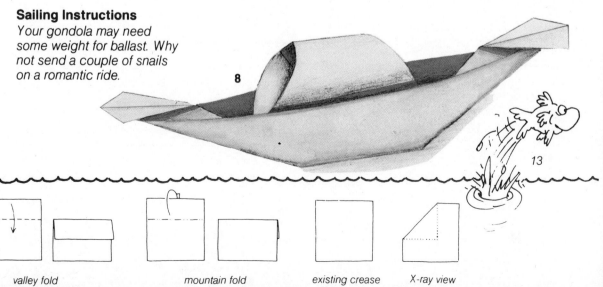

valley fold   *mountain fold*   *existing crease*   *X-ray view*

Rowing Boat

This is a simple little boat, complete with its own seat! A life-size replica would certainly be seaworthy, but you can have lots of fun even with this small version.

1.
Cut an A4 sheet of paper in half lengthwise. This is done by first folding the paper in half to find the centre. You can actually make two boats from one sheet of A4 paper.

2.
Fold the top end down approximately one-third of the length of the paper as shown.

3.
Fold in half lengthwise and place the model so that it faces you lengthwise.

4.
Fold the top edge (top flap) down to 5 mm from the bottom edge. Do the same on the other side.

5.
Crease fold at a 45-degree angle in the approximate position shown, folding over and behind along the same crease. Do this two or three times.

6.
Fold back to the horizontal position.

7.
Open the model out and lift the top flap from the centre outwards along the crease lines.

14

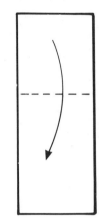

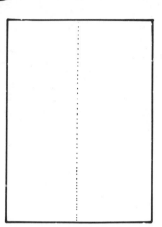

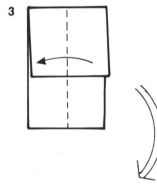

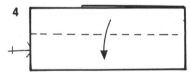

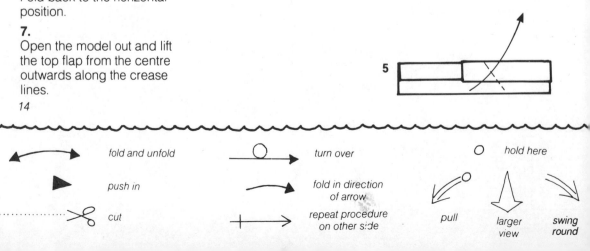

← → fold and unfold	○→ turn over	○ hold here
▶ push in	⟶ fold in direction of arrow	pull
·······✂ cut	⊢⟶ repeat procedure on other side	larger view · swing round

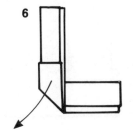

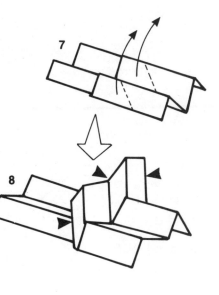

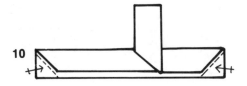

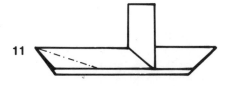

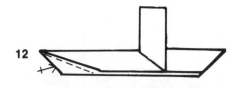

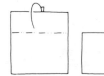

8.
Almost there! Push in the folds and make the model flat again.

9.
Fold the corners behind as shown.

10.
Repeat for the other side and also fold the inside corners inside the outer flaps.

11. and 12.
Fold the bow section again in exactly the same manner as steps 9 and 10, except that the folded inside corners should fold further as shown.

15

valley fold	*mountain fold*	*existing crease*	*X-ray view*

13.
With fingers and thumbs, open the model to form a small 'sail'.

14.
Fold the 'sail' down to form a seat.

15.
This is the view from above. Fold the sides down along the edge of the boat.

16.
Close-up view. Tuck the bottom flap behind and inside the flap underneath.

17.
Your completed rowing boat.

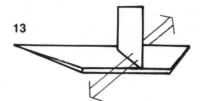

13

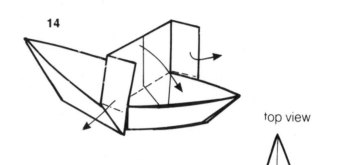

14

top view

15

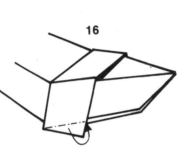

16

Sailing Instructions

Your rowing boat has no sail, but it will float perfectly on calm and choppy waters. You could make a huge ocean liner (page 41) and add little rowing boats to the sides of the ship as lifeboats.

17

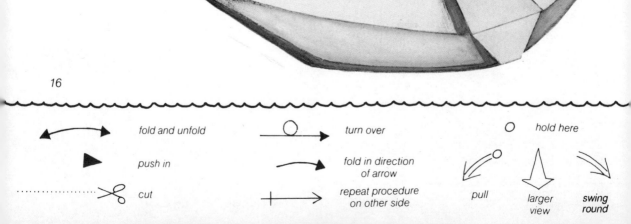

fold and unfold	turn over	⭕ hold here
push in	fold in direction of arrow	pull
✂ cut	repeat procedure on other side	larger view / swing round

Speedboat

On with your life jackets — now you can have your very own speedboat. This boat is ideal for the Great String Race (page 9) as it is designed to present very little resistance to water. Its snappy pointed bow will cut through the water at a great speed.

1.
The folding techniques for this model are similar to those for the rowing boat. Begin with half a sheet of A4 paper.

2.
Fold in half.

3.
Fold the flap up approximately one-sixth as shown.

4.
Fold the model in half lengthwise.

5.
With the model facing you, horizontally fold the top edge down as shown and repeat for the other side.

6.
Take between thumb and finger the area marked and pull upwards slightly.

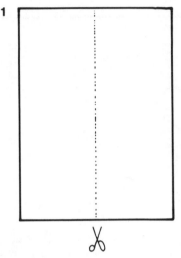

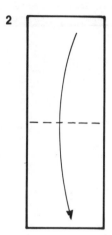

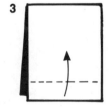

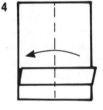

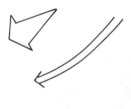

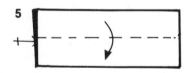

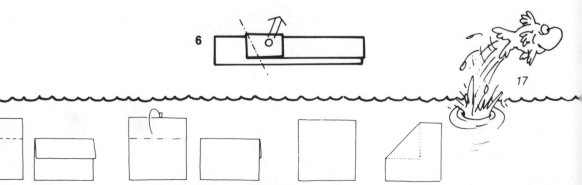

valley fold　　　　　mountain fold　　　　existing crease　　X-ray view

7.
With the model still flat, fold
the corners behind as shown.
Repeat for the other side and
also fold the inside corners
inside the outer flaps (the
same as for the rowing boat).
Repeat for the bow section.

8.
Fold the centre flap behind as
shown. Repeat for the other
side.

9.
Fold the centre flaps on both
sides behind again to secure
the windshield. Now pull
open the boat in the same
way as the rowing boat.

10.
Invert fold the leading edge of
the windshield in the
approximate position shown.

11.
Crease the windows as
shown.

12.
Your completed speedboat.

Sailing Instructions
*It's really quite simple. Pick
up your boat and gently place
it right-side-up on the water.
It should then float happily
until your friend with the
paper aircraft carrier blows it
out of the water.*

fold and unfold		turn over		hold here
push in		fold in direction of arrow		
cut		repeat procedure on other side	pull	larger view	swing round

Sailing Boat

Off you go into the sunset with this great little boat. It's ideal for the bath or boating pond or even the kitchen sink.

1.
Again, this model is similar to the rowing boat. Begin with a half length of A4 paper.

2.
Fold across in half as shown.

3.
Fold the sides of the top flap in as shown, pushing in the corners and flattening them.

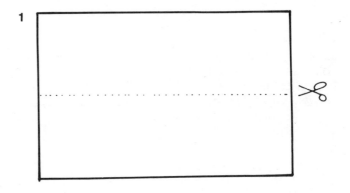

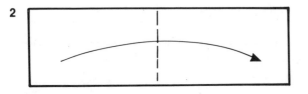

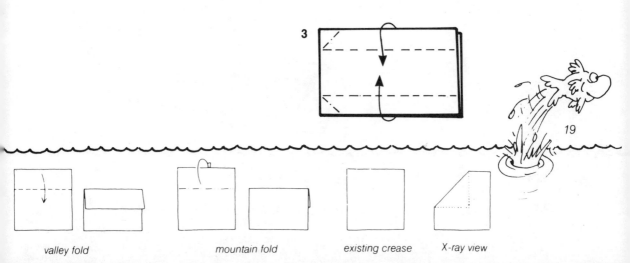

valley fold   mountain fold   existing crease   X-ray view

4.
Fold horizontally in half.

5.
Larger view. Fold as shown and repeat for the other side

6.
Crease fold at a 45-degreee angle as for the rowing boat (step 5), folding over and behind along the same crease. Do this two or three times. Fold back to the horizonal position.

7. and 8.
Fold back the side edges of the sail to give it rigidity.

9.
Fold the hull section in the same way as the rowing boat. Fold the corners behind. Repeat for the other side and also fold the inside corners inside the outer flaps. Fold the bow section in the same way. By holding the hull, open out the sail.

10. and 10a.
Your completed sailing boat.

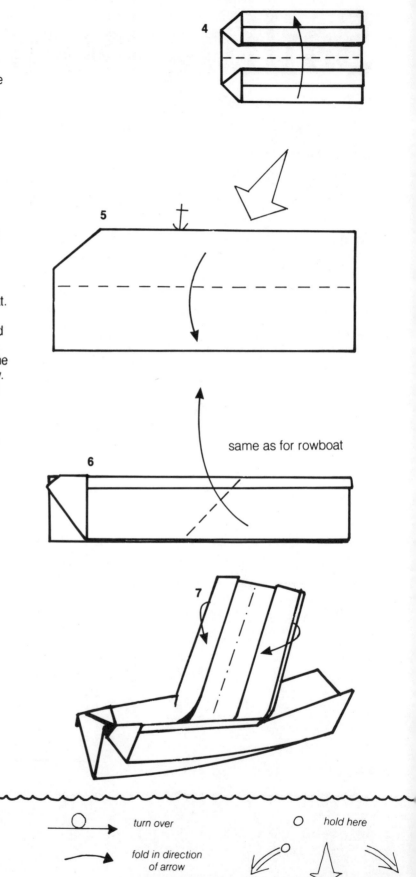

same as for rowboat

↔ fold and unfold	⟶○⟶ turn over	○ hold here
▶ push in	⟶ fold in direction of arrow	pull
⋯✂ cut	+⟶ repeat procedure on other side	larger view swing round

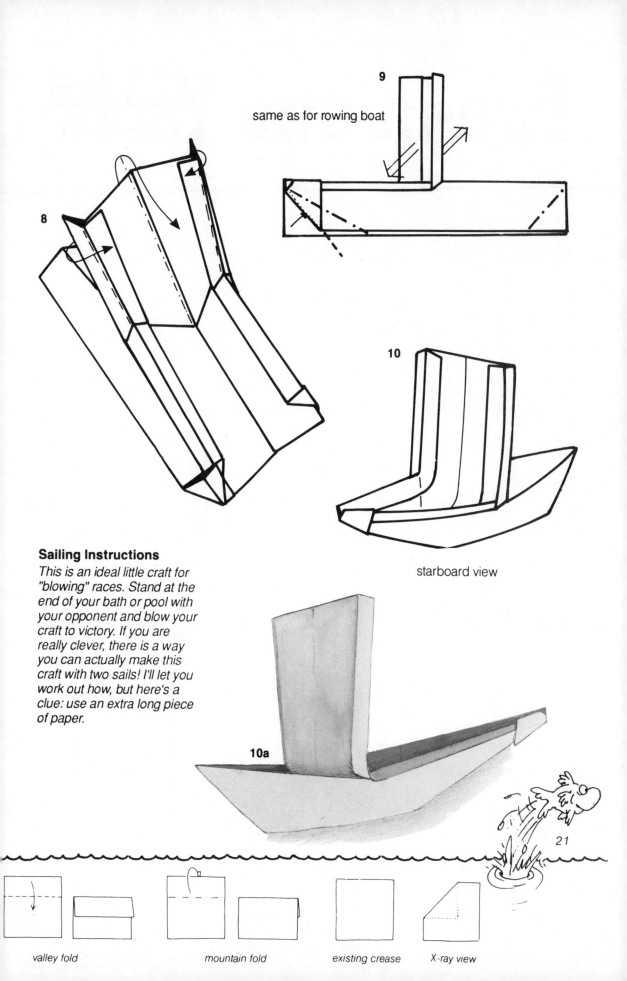

9

same as for rowing boat

8

10

starboard view

Sailing Instructions

This is an ideal little craft for "blowing" races. Stand at the end of your bath or pool with your opponent and blow your craft to victory. If you are really clever, there is a way you can actually make this craft with two sails! I'll let you work out how, but here's a clue: use an extra long piece of paper.

10a

21

valley fold   mountain fold   existing crease   X-ray view

Two-in-one Yacht

This is your own yacht which comes complete with a jib and can actually double as a small catamaran! The jib can also be used as a keel to keep your yacht stable in rougher seas.

1.
Fold an A4 sheet of paper to make a square.

2.
Cut off the end but don't throw it away! You'll need it for the jib, keel or catamaran.

3.
Make a rabbit ear fold as shown.

4.
Mountain fold in half.

5.
Push in the hull section.

6.
Almost there. Turn the model right-way-up.

7.
It should look like this rather boring sailing boat.

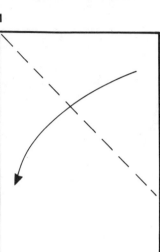

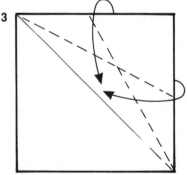

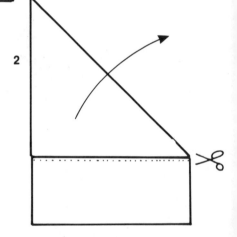

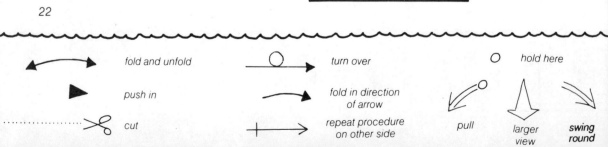

fold and unfold

push in

cut

turn over

fold in direction of arrow

repeat procedure on other side

hold here

pull

larger view

swing round

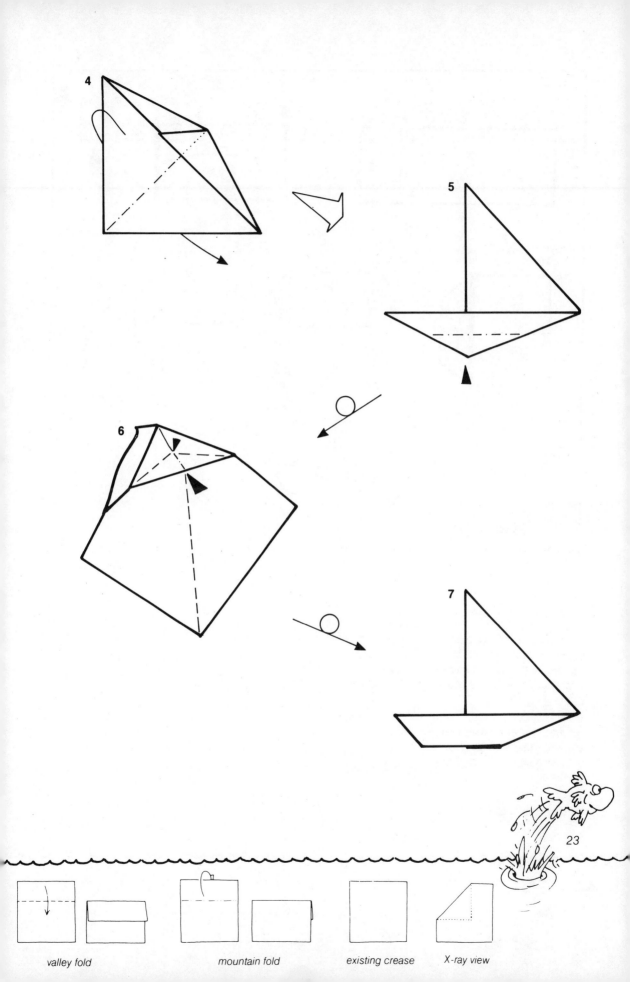

4

5

6

7

valley fold

mountain fold

existing crease

X-ray view

23

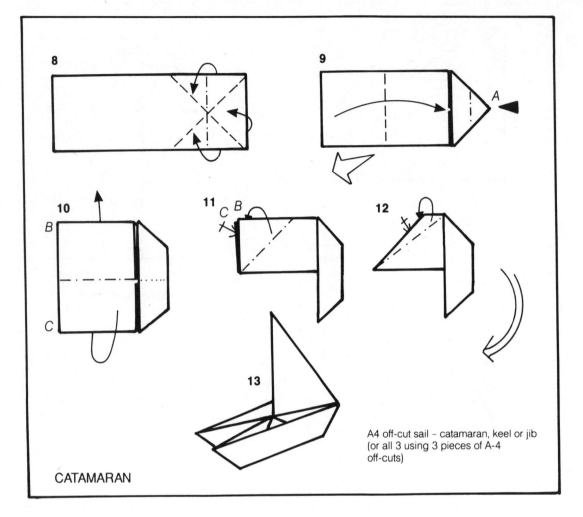

8 **9**

10 **11** C B **12**

13

A4 off-cut sail – catamaran, keel or jib
(or all 3 using 3 pieces of A-4
off-cuts)

CATAMARAN

8.
Now take the off-cut piece of
paper and fold one end to
make a waterbomb base—
see step 1 to 6 of the sea-
plane (page 33).

9.
Fold the other end across as
shown. Push in A as shown
(you should be good at this
by now).

10.
Larger view. Fold behind.

11.
Fold corners B and C to the
inside.

12.
Fold these corners in again to
make a sail. Turn the model
right-way-up.

13.
This is your completed
catamaran.

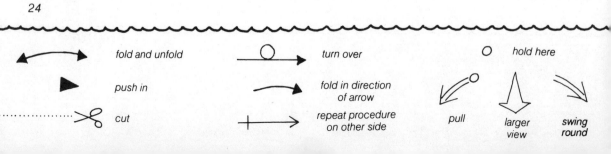

fold and unfold   turn over   O   hold here

push in   fold in direction
of arrow

cut   repeat procedure
on other side   pull   larger
view   swing
round

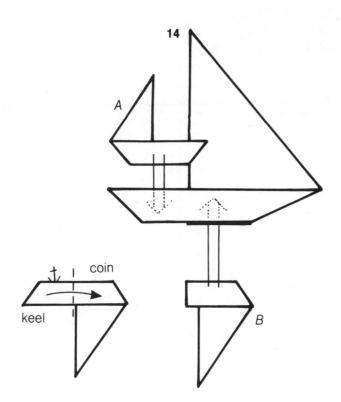

14.
The catamaran can be slotted inside the main boat as shown and held in place with a small piece of tape. Alternatively, turn the catamaran upside down and fold the ends across. Slot a coin inside the keel for weight and slot the keel inside the hull, holding with tape.

15.
Your completed yacht with jib and keel.

15a.
Your catamaran on its merry way.

Sailing Instructions
With the keel, this craft can go out on the open water with no trouble. Don't lose it in a strong headwind! If nobody likes the 'cut of your jib' then take it off!

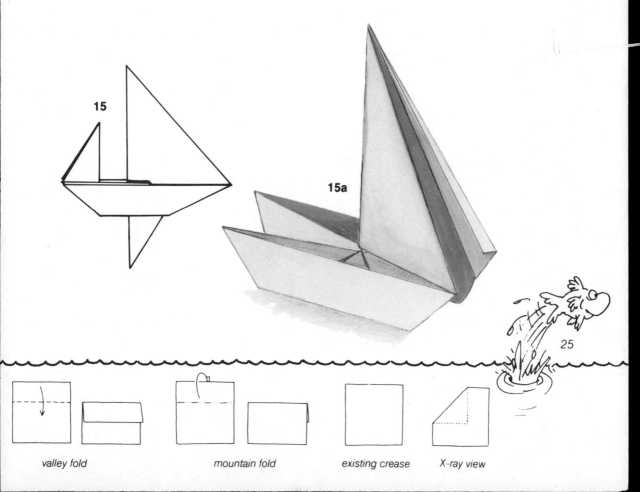

| valley fold | mountain fold | existing crease | X-ray view |

Catamaran

Your catamaran is similar to the one which the United States used for the America's Cup challenge in 1988, and it floats very well. The sail section we have designed is more for style than anything and there are ways to make a more efficient sail. I'll leave that to your inventive mind.

1. and 1a.
Make a square from an A4 piece of paper and keep the offcut.

2.
Fold the square diagonally both ways and then fold in half. Then, with the paper opened out again, fold the sides in to meet the centre crease.

3.
Mountain fold in half as shown.

4.
Fold the flap up approximately one-third of the way as shown.

5.
Pull out the inside points.

6.
Almost there! Flatten the fold and repeat steps 4–6 for the other side.

1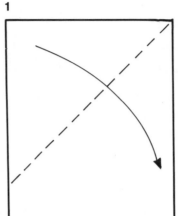

1a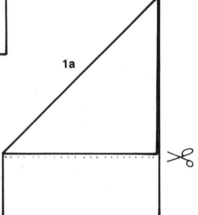

2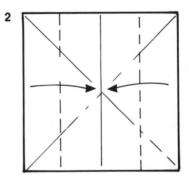

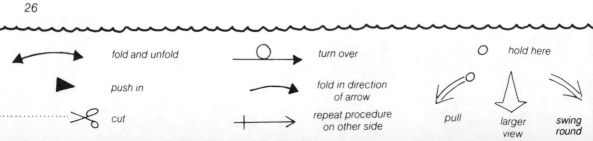

fold and unfold

push in

cut

turn over

fold in direction of arrow

repeat procedure on other side

hold here

pull

larger view

swing round

3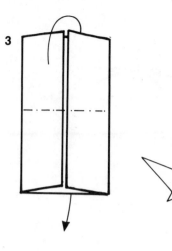

4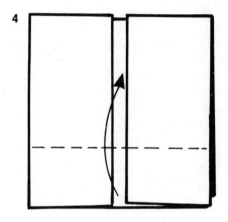

5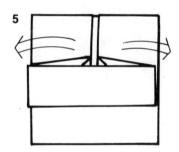

6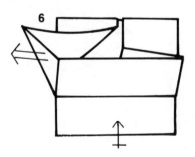

27

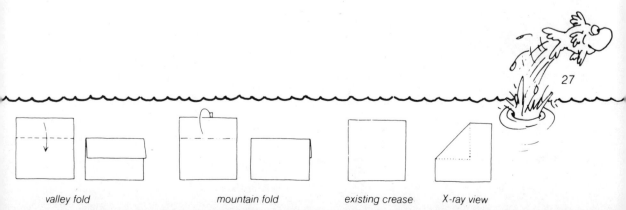

valley fold   *mountain fold*   *existing crease*   *X-ray view*

7. and 7a.
Fold as shown on both sides
to form a deck.

8.
This is what it should look like.

9.
Using the offcut piece for the
sail, fold the corner up as
shown.

10.
Fold the corner again.

11.
Fold the whole left-hand point
down as shown.

12.
Fold the sail across again,
creasing the edge part way.

13.
Push corner in. A bit tricky.

14.
Lift sail to vertical position.

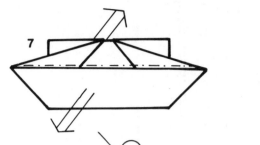

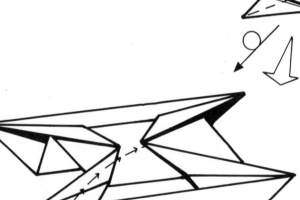

FINISHED SAIL

↔	fold and unfold	⟶ turn over	O hold here
▶	push in	⟶ fold in direction of arrow	pull
✂	cut	+⟶ repeat procedure on other side	larger view — swing round

SAIL SECTION

9

10

11

12

13 top view

14

15.
The sail should look like this.
The bottom of the sail,
marked A, slots under the flap
at one end of the boat (figure 8).

16.
Your completed catamaran.

16

Sailing Instructions
*Your craft should sail well
under light winds. You can
open out the hull section with
your fingers to add bouyancy.*

29

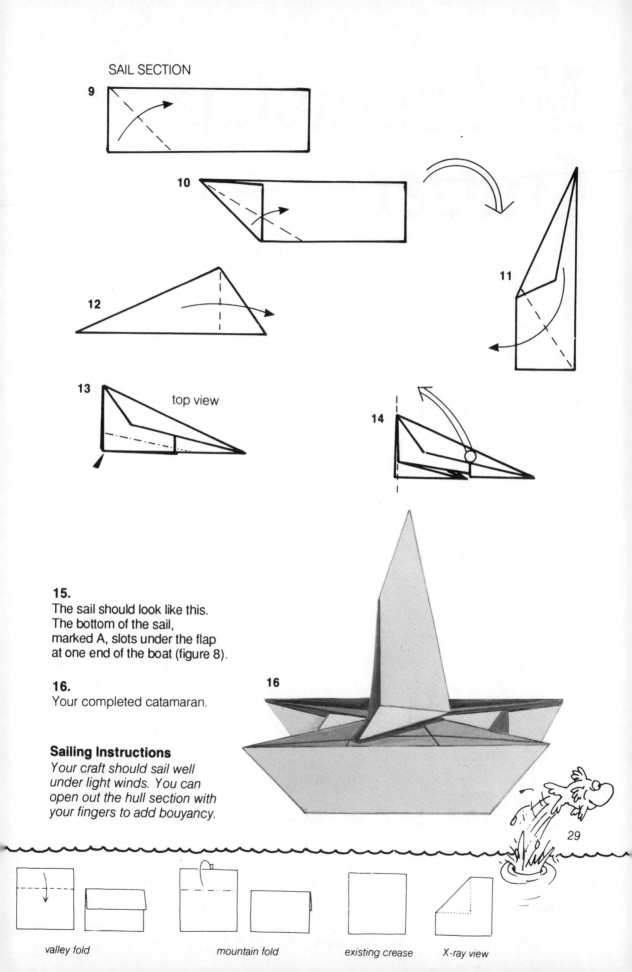

valley fold   *mountain fold*   *existing crease*   *X-ray view*

Million-dollar Cruiser

Next time you visit a marina, keep your eye open for one of these sophisticated and classy vessels. Even if you don't see one, I'm sure you've seen them on television—the ones owned by millionaires and rock stars. Now it's time for you to step up to luxury. Make your very own cruiser and be the envy of your neighbourhood.

1.
Begin with a square and fold the sides into the centre as shown.

2.
Fold the corners behind as indicated, then fold lengthwise in half.

3.
Larger view. Inverse fold as shown along the inside folds.

4.
Push in the hull of the boat.

5.
Almost there!

6.
It should look like this. Invert fold the 'sail'.

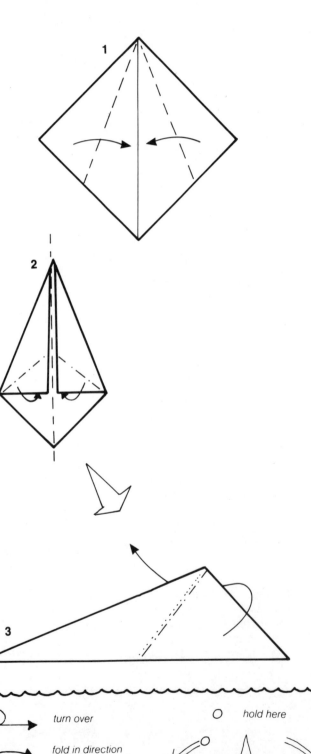

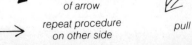

⟷ fold and unfold	→○ turn over	○ hold here	
▶ push in	→ fold in direction of arrow	pull	
····✂ cut	+→ repeat procedure on other side	larger view	swing round

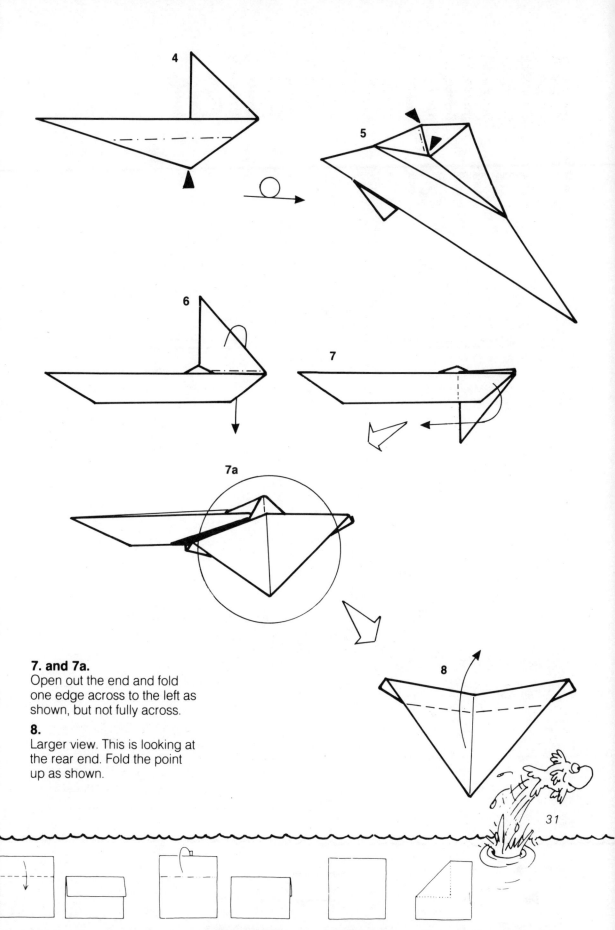

7. and 7a.
Open out the end and fold
one edge across to the left as
shown, but not fully across.

8.
Larger view. This is looking at
the rear end. Fold the point
up as shown.

31

valley fold   mountain fold   existing crease   X-ray view

9.
Place the thumb behind area
A and fold the flap to the left.

10.
Repeat for the left side, then
fold points B and C together.

11.
You now have a sleek cruiser
in which to carry your fortune.

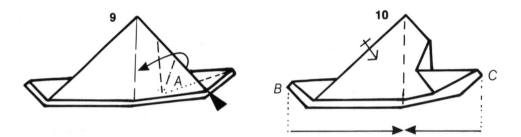

Sailing Instructions
*This craft floats well if kept
upright. Its ultra-sleek design
will make it ideal for the string
races too.*

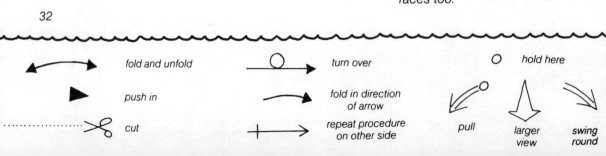

fold and unfold

push in

cut

turn over

fold in direction
of arrow

repeat procedure
on other side

hold here

pull

larger
view

swing
round

Seaplane

While we're on the water, why not build this great model sea-plane—if folded correctly it will fly and float too! You can build a gigantic aircraft carrier (page 44), spray it watertight with lacquer and then land your aircraft on board. If you miss, your plane will be safe because the huge skis will keep it afloat.

1.
Begin with A4 paper creased in half lengthwise. Fold the corner in as shown, then unfold.

2.
Fold the other corner in, then unfold.

3.
Fold behind across the centre crease where the two diagonal folds meet.

4.
Place your finger where all the creases meet and push down. All the sides will pop up. Bring the sides in as shown.

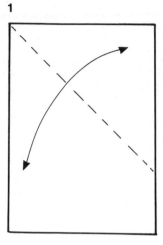

1

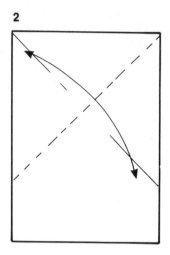

2

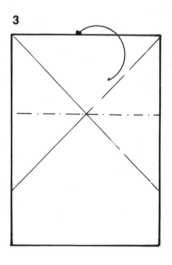

3

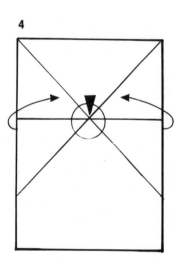

4

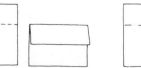

valley fold   mountain fold   existing crease   X-ray view

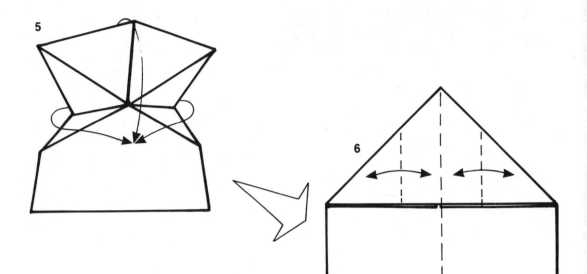

5

6

7

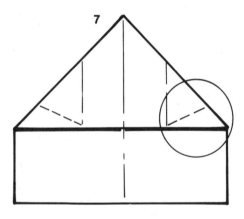

7a

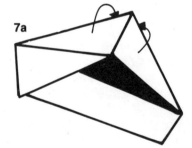

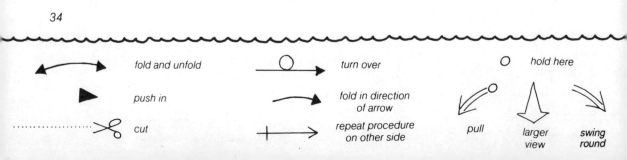

↤↦	*fold and unfold*	⊙→	*turn over*	◯	*hold here*
▶	*push in*	→▶	*fold in direction of arrow*	↙◯	*pull*
·········✂	*cut*	┼→	*repeat procedure on other side*	⇩ *larger view*	⇲ *swing round*

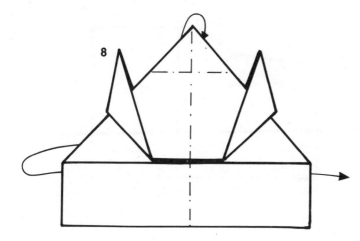

5.
Almost there. Flatten the top edge down. It should all come together nicely.

6.
Crease fold the top flaps as shown.

7.
Crease fold the two points then reverse fold by turning the points inside out.

7a.
Most of the folded model has to be opened out to accommodate this fold. It will fold back into shape easily.

8.
Fold the nose behind. Then fold the model behind lengthwise in half.

9.
Fold edges behind and push corner in.

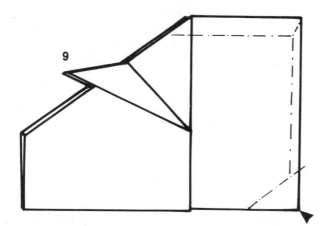

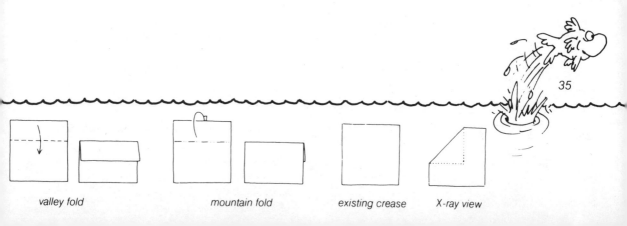

valley fold   mountain fold   existing crease   X-ray view

10.
Fold the wings down as shown.

11.
Swing the model round to face you. Push the corner in approximately 5 mm above the wing line. Then fold the flaps up. Fold the complete trailing edge up as shown. This will ensure the model is watertight when landing.

12.
Your completed seaplane. Open out the waterskis with your fingers. For weight, tape a twenty pence piece to the nose. This may not be necessary, depending on how high the trailing edge is folded. Experiment to find the best fold and weight.

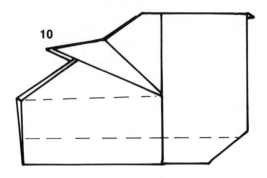

10

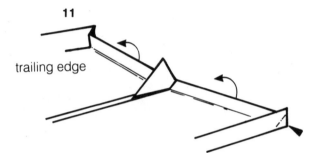

11

trailing edge

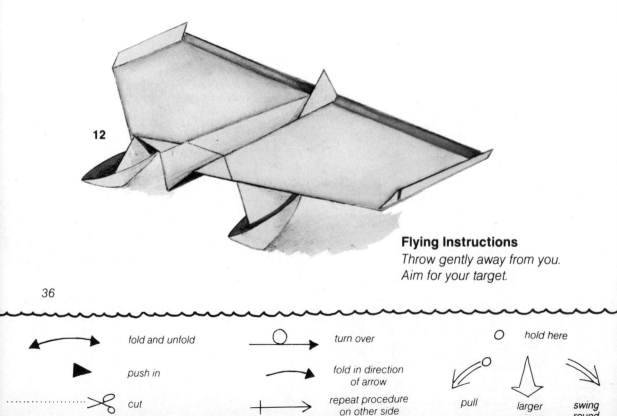

12

Flying Instructions
Throw gently away from you.
Aim for your target.

←→ fold and unfold	○→ turn over	O hold here
▶ push in	fold in direction of arrow	pull · larger view · swing round
✂ cut	repeat procedure on other side	

Pirate Ship

'Ahoy there, me 'earties!'
You'll have to walk the plank if
you can't make this great
model.

1.
Take a piece of A4 paper and
fold it in half.

2.
Fold the bottom corners and
the corners of the top flap in
as shown.

3.
Fold again.

4.
Turn over and fold the top flap
twice, as shown.

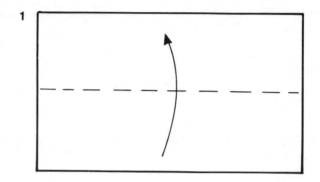

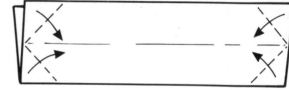

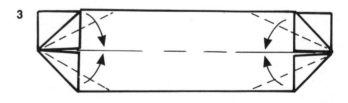

37

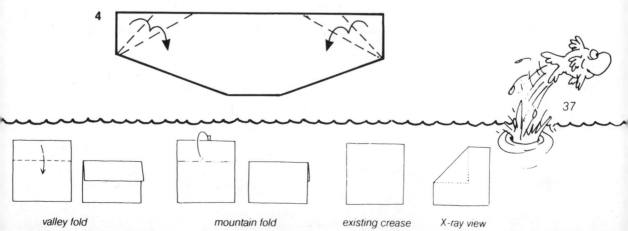

valley fold   *mountain fold*   *existing crease*   *X-ray view*

5.
It should look like this. Fold the top half of the top flap down.

6.
Larger view. Push in the base of the hull.

6a.
Frog diver's view.

7.
Reverse fold the bow. Inverse fold the stern.

8.
Fold the bow point up again as shown. Inverse fold the stern again.

9.
Open out the boat. It should look like this.

10.
Cut another A4 sheet of paper in half lengthwise. Cut the half piece into two quarter strips. These will be the sails.

11.
For each quarter strip, make length and width halfway creases and then fold the corners in.

12.
Fold the corners in again.

13.
Fold across in half.

14.
Fold up the points on each side to the horizontal position.

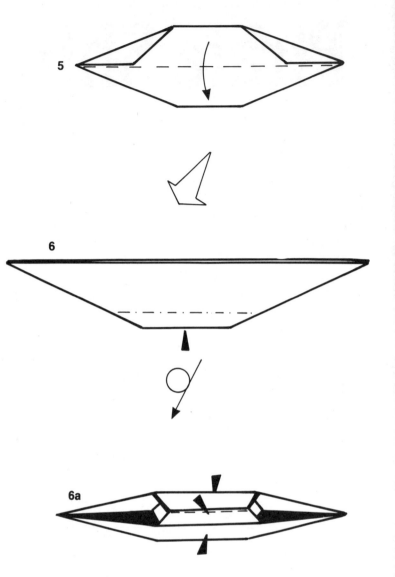

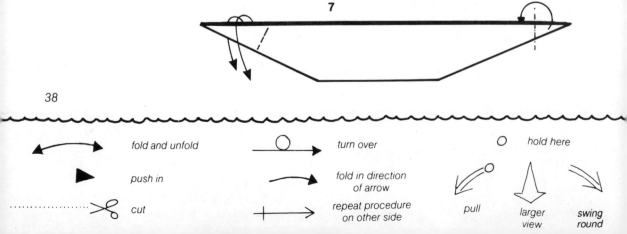

fold and unfold	turn over	hold here	
push in	fold in direction of arrow		
cut	repeat procedure on other side	pull	larger view	swing round

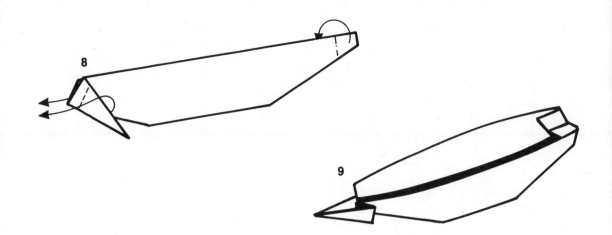

8

9

SAIL SECTION

10

11

12

13

14

valley fold   mountain fold   existing crease   X-ray view

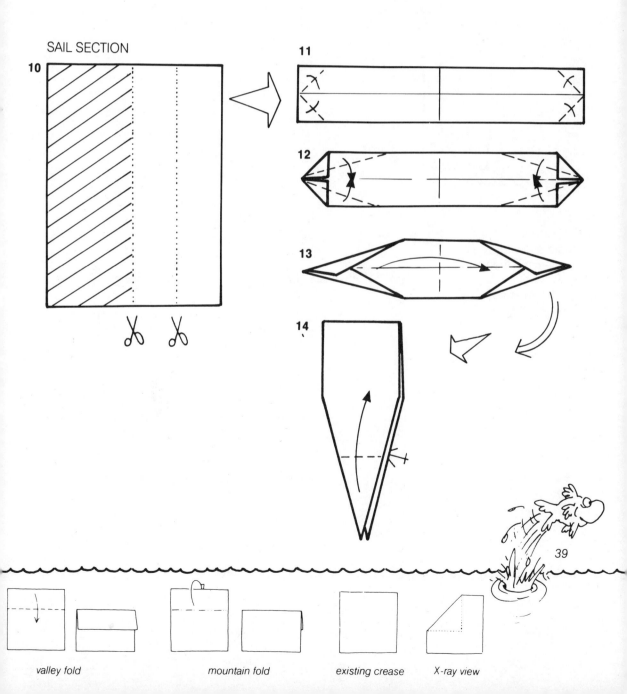

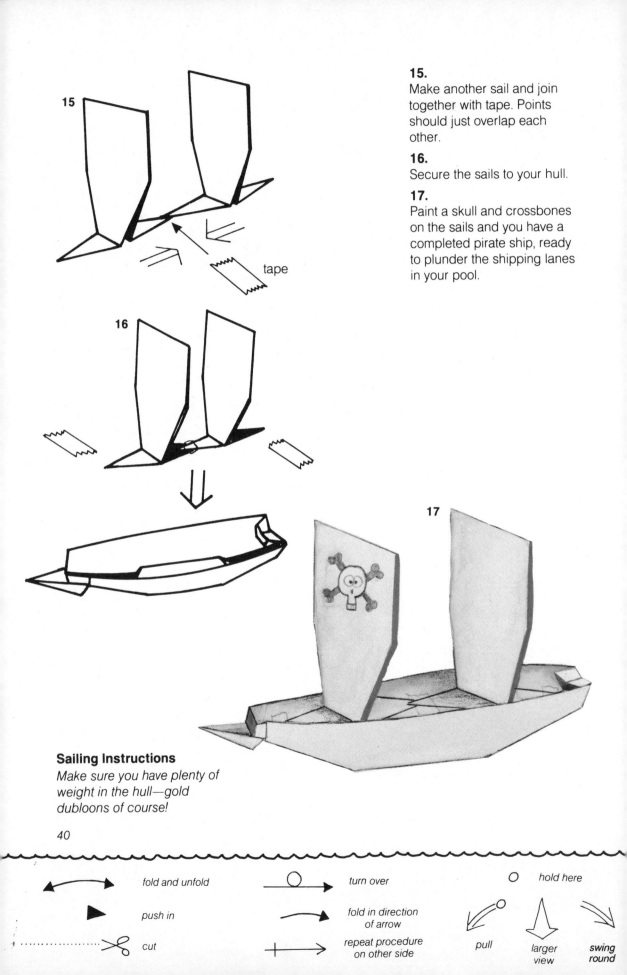

15.
Make another sail and join together with tape. Points should just overlap each other.

16.
Secure the sails to your hull.

17.
Paint a skull and crossbones on the sails and you have a completed pirate ship, ready to plunder the shipping lanes in your pool.

tape

Sailing Instructions
Make sure you have plenty of weight in the hull—gold dubloons of course!

fold and unfold	turn over
push in	fold in direction of arrow
cut	repeat procedure on other side

hold here

pull   larger view   swing round

Ocean Liner

Isn't it time you took a cruise? Perhaps to the South Pacific or the Bahamas? This ocean liner could certainly go on a cruise, even if it is only round your boating pond!

Use half a sheet of A4 to start with. The model will end up quite small but, having mastered the folds, you could then use a large sheet of thin card.

1.
Cut the sheet of paper in half lengthwise.

2.
Using one half, crease fold lengthwise in half then unfold. Fold the edges in to meet the centre crease.

3.
Fold the ends in at one-third intervals, first the left end, then the right end.

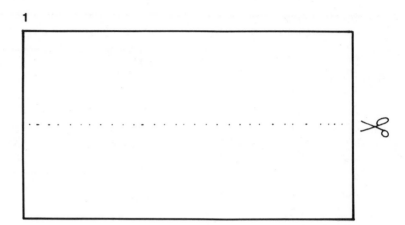

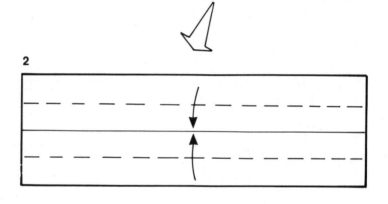

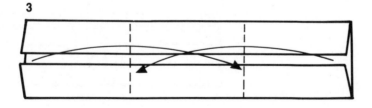

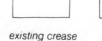

41

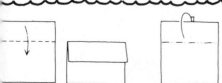

valley fold   *mountain fold*   *existing crease*   *X-ray view*

4.
Fold the top left end across to the right. Fold the flap underneath from the right to the left.

5.
Fold the edges in, squashing the corners flat.

6.
Valley fold the model lengthwise in half.

7.
Lift the inside strip on the left and invert fold for the smoke stack as shown.

8.
Almost there. Now, repeat for the other side.

9.
Fold the corners up to make the hull. Then fold the top railing down. Repeat railing fold for the other side.

10.
Your completed ocean liner. Fold a model big enough and you'll be able to take your cat on an ocean voyage!

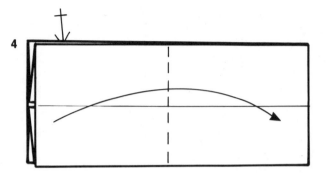

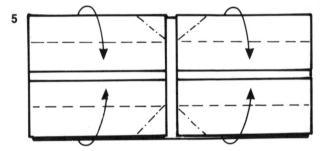

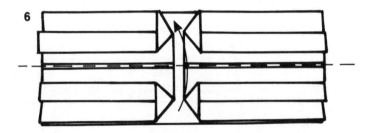

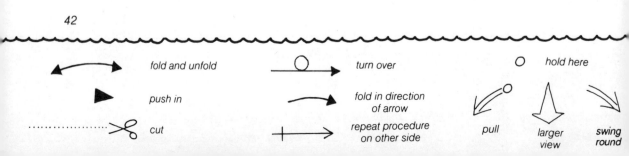

fold and unfold

push in

cut

turn over

fold in direction of arrow

repeat procedure on other side

hold here

pull

larger view

swing round

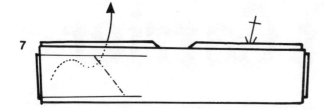

7

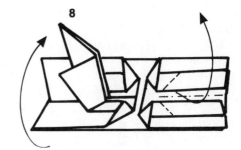

8

9

Sailing Instructions

You will probably need ballast—try a couple of coins (or a snail or two, depending on the size of your liner). There is a way you can convert the smoke stacks into a cabin like Noah's Ark, but I'll leave that to your ingenuity! (Clue: Inverse fold the stacks towards the centre of the ship so they overlap, then open out the ship so that the stacks form a roof.)

10

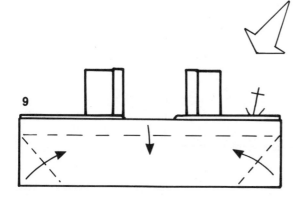

43

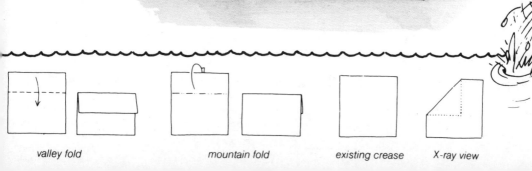

valley fold   mountain fold   existing crease   X-ray view

Aircraft Carrier

Just imagine—you are flying almost blind, searching for your aircraft carrier. An artificial electron radiation cloud smothers the ocean area, rendering your radar inoperative. You are Captain Swift, Top Gun leader, trying desperately to spot your craft. 'I have visual sighting . . . I'm closing in . . . '

Suddenly, you are shocked out of your ejector seat . . . 'I can't believe it . . . the HMS Immovable *is made of . . . of . . . paper!'*

1.
Use foolscap paper. Fold in half across.

2.
Measure 4 cm up from the bottom, then crease fold horizontally the top flap and the one behind. Then push the corners inwards diagonally. Fold the top flaps down again.

3.
Fold the flap behind up.

4.
Fold the corners down.

5.
Fold the top down as shown.

6.
Fold up as shown.

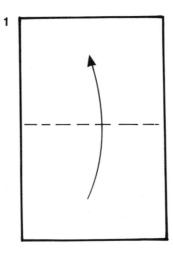

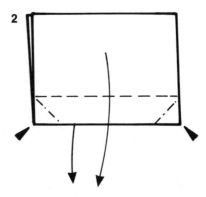

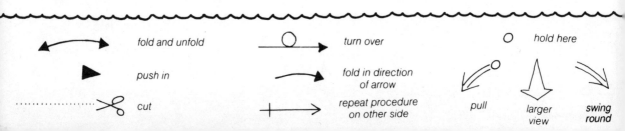

fold and unfold	turn over
push in	fold in direction of arrow
cut	repeat procedure on other side

hold here

pull

larger view

swing round

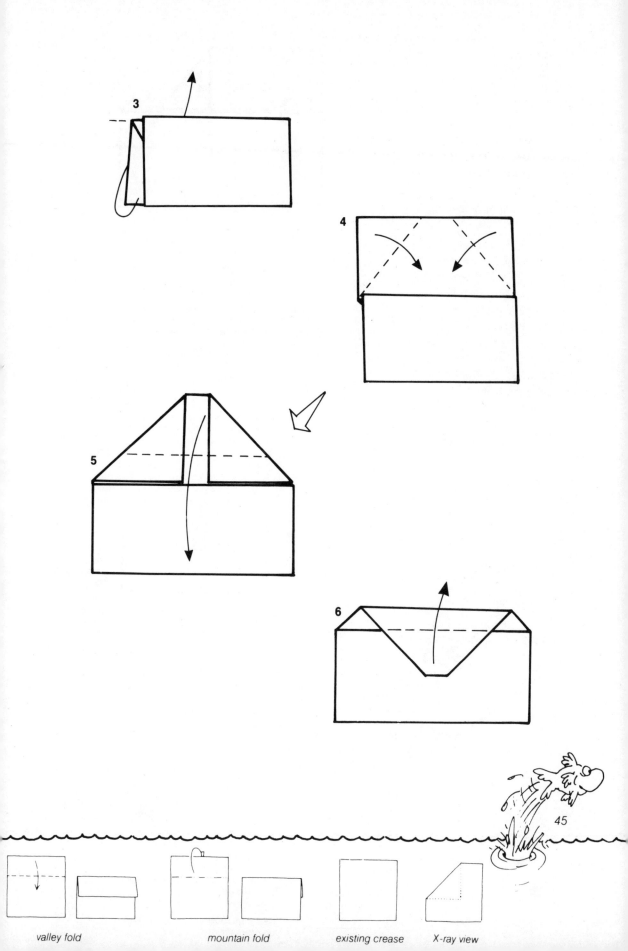

3

4

5

6

45

valley fold   mountain fold   existing crease   X-ray view

7.
Tuck fingers behind the top flap and pull the sides towards the centre.

8.
Crease fold along XX then unfold. Fold up along YY and tuck the edge under.

9.
Fold up the control tower.

10.
Tuck the runway under the control tower flap as shown. Open the hull and create a new fold as shown (XX). This will create a wider hull in which to place ballast (which can be a heavy pen, drill bit, sand, etc.). Tape the control tower section to the runway to secure the vessel. Fold corners A and B behind.

11.
Your completed aircraft carrier.

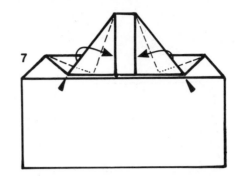

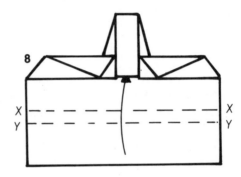

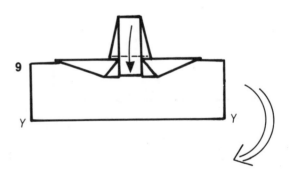

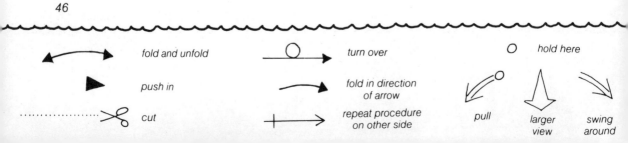

fold and unfold	turn over
push in	fold in direction of arrow
cut	repeat procedure on other side

hold here

pull

larger view

swing around

Sailing Instructions

This ship works well with A4 paper. Larger sheets of paper or cardboard can be used but the ballast will have to be increased to keep the vessel upright. If the ship tilts, make a keel out of card with a coin taped to its end.

11

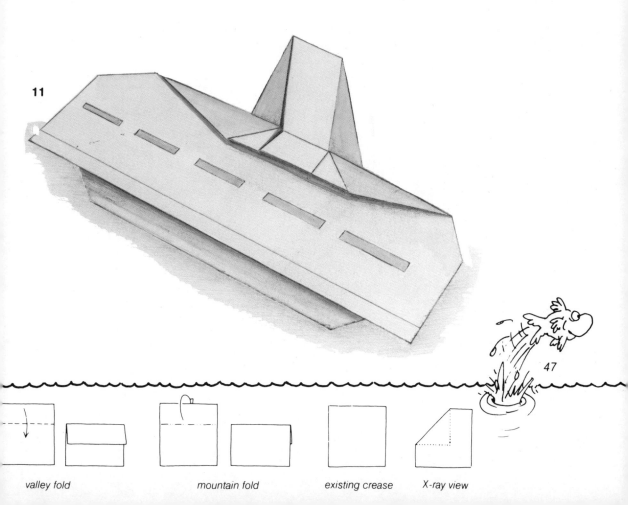

valley fold   mountain fold   existing crease   X-ray view